Contents

Introduction

The Mental Warm-up Activities provide a structured scheme of work for developing mental mathematics strategies. The daily activities have been written to practise key mental maths skill, and address these using a variety of tactics:

- practising pre-requisite skills (e.g. partitioning numbers: 8 is 7 and 1, 6 and 2, 5 and 3, 4 and 4)

- building on two or more of these skills to develop a new strategy (e.g. adding 17 + 8 by partitioning 8 into 3 and 5, and knowing that 17 + 3 = 20)

- practising and extending known strategies (e.g. 27 + 8 =)

- using known strategies as pre-requisites for a new set of strategies (e.g. related to a different operation)

- developing a 'memory bank' of key facts (e.g. addition bonds to 10, doubles to 10)

- using key facts to develop further strategies (e.g. 3 + 3 = 6 so 3 + 4 = 7)

How to use this book

To allow the teacher flexibility, the book is broken down into two sections:

Unit specific activities

For each Number Unit there are two whole class activities. Some of these relate directly to skills or sub-skills for that Unit. Some activities practise more general skills, and these will develop in strands throughout the book (a skills chart mapping this development is included on pages 70 to 72). Often the two activities provided will be enough to cover the work required for that Unit.

Activity bank

For Number Units that last longer than two days, or for Shape, Space and Measures Units, the teacher can select supplementary activities from the Bank provided at the back of the book. The Activity Bank includes a wide variety of activities that address key skills under topic headings (e.g.

counting, addition, place-value). The activities in the bank can be used at any time alongside any topic, and often you will wish to revisit them throughout the year.

Together, these two types of activity will provide enough activities for one warm-up every day.

The activities

The activities are of three types:

Open-ended

These are activities where there may be several ways of getting a 'right' answer. Often a key benefit of the activity will be the discussion which the children have with you and each other about which strategies they have used. This is a good opportunity to go through several different ways of doing something with the whole class, so that different methods or techniques are shared and discussed.

Closed

These activities have one correct answer and usually, one preferred strategy to use. So, for example, when adding 9 to a 2-digit number, the activity may practise the specific technique of adding 10 and taking one away.

Memorising

These activities are designed to help children memorise a particular set of number facts, e.g. doubles of numbers to 10, addition bonds. Eventually each child will have a set of memorised facts that they know by heart. Certain key activities appear several times during the book to help reinforce these skills.

Generic activities

Most of the activities use similar formats and structures from Unit to Unit, and children will become familiar with these. These 'generic' activities are described in more detail on pages iv to vi.

Also included in each section are a number of the week, and a word of the week or a shape of the week. These can be used to develop children's use of the language and vocabulary of number both spoken ('tell me something about this week's number') and written ('write three things about this week's shape').

The number of the week can be used to develop mental dexterity, consolidate concepts and skills studied in a given Number Unit, and to develop the use and understanding of the language of number. For each number some sample tasks and facts are given.

The shape of the week can be used to increase awareness of the properties of shape and space, and to encourage the use of the associated language.

The word of the week can be used to develop use and understanding of the vocabulary of mathematics, and to consolidate language associated with the Unit being studied. Sometimes the 'word of the week' relates to vocabulary in the relevant Unit, sometimes the word is included to rehearse vocabulary met in the past or introduce new vocabulary. Children should be encouraged both to hear the word being used in different contexts, and to use the word in responses and statements.

Working partners

At the beginning of the year (or each term), place the children in pairs as 'working partners'. The pairs do not necessarily have to be matched in ability – two children of different abilities can help each other. Over time the children will become used to working together, and a 'regular' partner will save you time when setting up the activities.

Generic Activities

Many of the activities throughout this book follow common formats and structures. This will enable you to set up and run a particular activity quickly, and over time, the children will become used to the 'rules' involved. The 'generic' activities are described here in more detail.

Bingo

- The children work with their partners. They write several 'bingo' numbers on a piece of paper, circling each one. The numbers should match a certain criterion (e.g. less than 10).
- The teacher generates numbers at random (e.g. by selecting cards from a shuffled set).
- The teacher chooses a child to perform an operation on the card (e.g. saying the bond to make ten).
- The children can cross out one of their 'bingo' numbers if it matches the answer.
- The first pair to cross out all their numbers wins.

Cross-puzzles

- The teacher draws a cross on the board, with three squares in each arm, writing a letter (a to e) in each square.
- The children are given clues for each letter (e.g. the number two more than 8).
- The children work to fill in all the correct numbers.
- Between each pair of numbers the children write a sign (e.g. +, −, =), to make the whole cross consistent.

Imagine

- The children shut their eyes and imagine a number of objects.
- The teacher performs an operation on their objects (e.g. removing some).
- The children say the answer (e.g. how many are left).
- Check the answers with the class.

Letter prices

- Children work with their partners.
- The teacher assigns values to each letter of the alphabet.
- Children find the total value of different words (e.g. their names).

Missing numbers
- Children work with their partners.
- The teacher writes a sequence of numbers on the board, with one or more numbers missing.
- The pairs decide which numbers are missing.

Number lines
- The teacher draws a two-column table on the board, and in the left-hand column writes numbers.
- Children are invited to the front to perform an operation on a number (e.g. adding 10), writing the answer in the right-hand column.
- Check with the class.

Some wrong!
- The teacher writes a series of calculations on the board (e.g. bonds to 10) one or more of which are incorrect.
- Allow the children a few minutes to decide which are incorrect.
- Go through them on the board, asking different children whether each is correct or incorrect.

Round the class
- The teacher points to a child and says a number.
- That child responds with a new number (e.g. by counting on one, or back ten).
- The first child chooses another who continued the count, and so on.
- A good rule is to let boys choose girls and girls choose boys.

Show me
- Children work with their partners. Each pair has a set of number cards.
- The teacher calls out several calculations and the pairs match the answers with their cards (they can make 2-digit numbers by holding two cards together).

Speed track
- The teacher holds up ten flash cards in turn, each with a calculation on.
- The children write the answers.
- The teacher keeps up a good pace, and times the children.

- Check the answer with the class.
- These activities can be repeated during the year, with the children trying to beat their best times.

Story maths
- The teacher tells the children a story (e.g. involving money).
- Allow the children a few minutes to calculate the answer.
- Choose different children to say their answer, then check with the whole class.

Teddy pass

- Use a teddy bear, or other soft toy.
- The teacher passes the teddy to one child, and says a number.
- That child performs an operation on that number (e.g. add ten), and passes the teddy to a new child.
- The second child performs the same operation on the new number, and so on.

N1 Numbers to 100

Teddy pass

Counting in ones

A teddy bear

Give the teddy to one child, saying a number, e.g.
seventeen. They take the teddy and pass it to another
child, saying the number one more, e.g. *eighteen*.
That child passes the teddy on to another child, saying
the number one more, e.g. *nineteen*.
Keep passing the teddy like this.

Missing numbers

Counting in ones

Write a sequence of numbers on the
board, with one missing.
Give children 2 or 3 minutes to discover
the missing number. They must not shout
it out, but write the missing number on a
piece of paper and keep it hidden.

6, 7, 8, 9, 10
12, 13, 14, 15, 16

When you say, *Ready, steady, go!* they hold up their pieces of paper.
Count along the numbers on the board. Who wrote the correct number?
Play again, writing some different numbers on the board.

Number of the week

25

Sample tasks
- Count on and back in fives to and from our number.
- How many 10s and how many units in our number?
- How many of our number make 100?
- Add 1, 3, 5, ...
- Take 1, 5, 2, ...
- What is the number made by swapping (reversing) the digits?

Sample facts
- it is in the fives, the fifth five
- it is exactly halfway between 20 and 30
- it is an odd number
- it has a digit total of 7, and a digit difference of 3
- it is half of 50, a quarter of 100

N2 Place-value

Show me

Two less

Number cards (0 to 9), one set per pair

Ask the children to show you the number card that is
two less than 3; then 9; then 6; then 2; then 8; then 4;
then 11; then 10; then 5. For example, when you say *three*, they show
you the 1 card.

Stick there

Tens and units

Two dice and cubes

Put the children into two teams.
Write *T* and *U* on the board for each
team. The children take turns to
throw the dice for their team.

They write the number they have thrown on the board in either the tens
or the units column for their team, trying to make the largest number
possible.

When each team has written two digits on the board, they all read the
2-digit number they have created.

Compare numbers. Which is the larger? That team gets a cube.

Play until one team has seven cubes.

Shape of the week

Sample tasks
- it is a solid (3-d) shape
- some bricks and some boxes are cube shaped
- it has 6 faces which are all squares
- it has 8 corners
- it has 12 edges
- two cubes joined together make
  a cuboid

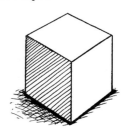

N3 Addition

Story maths

Coin recognition

Several 1p, 2p and 5p coins

Tell the children a brief story. *One day, Ilesh was out walking on the beach near his home. He was walking along the edge of the water when something glistening in the sand beneath the waves caught his eye. It was two coins! Very excited, Ilesh picked the coins up. He realised that they added up to 10p in all. Which two coins had he found?* Give the children 2 or 3 minutes' thinking time and then take suggestions. Use real coins to demonstrate the answer. Tell a similar story with different coins.

Number lines

Addition pairs to 10

Write on the board *This and what makes 10?*

Then write these numbers in a column on the left-hand side of the board: 5, 4, 7, 10, 8, 3, 6, 9, 2, 0, 1.

> This and what makes 10?
> 5
> 4
> 7
> 10

Go down the list and choose different children to write alongside each the number that, when added to it, makes 10.

Number of the week

Sample tasks
- Count in twos to our number, and beyond.
- Count in tens from our number. Repeat for fives.
- Say two numbers which add to our number. e.g. 1 and 9.
- Add our number to 3, 17, 24, ...
- Take our number from 17, 11, 23, ...

Sample facts
- pairs which make 10 are 0 and 10, 1 and 9, 2 and 8, ...
- it is the first 2-digit number
- it is in the 'twos', the 'tens' and the 'fives'
- it is the number of 1p coins in 10p, the number of 10p coins in £1
- it is the number of 10 cm strips in 1 metre
- it is the number of toes we each have

Money

One wrong!

Addition pairs to 6

A number line, Blu-tack

Unpeg 6 from the number line and Blu-tack it on the board. Write three addition pairs on the board, e.g. 2 + 4 = 6, 3 + 3 = 6, 5 + 2 = 6.

Tell the children that one of these addition pairs is wrong. Give them 3 or 4 minutes to work out which pair is wrong. Then they can mark the teacher's work on the board, ticking the additions that are correct and putting a cross beside the one that is wrong.

Letter prices

Counting in twos

1p, 2p, 5p and 10p coins

Stick 1p, 2p, 5p, 10p coins on the board. Choose a child to come and write their name on the board, e.g. *Annie.*

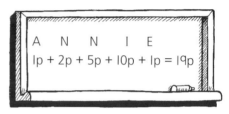

A N N I E
1p + 2p + 5p + 10p + 1p = 19p

Ask the children how much it costs to buy her name if the first letter costs 1p, the second costs 2p, the third costs 5p, the fourth costs 10p, the fifth costs 1p, the sixth costs 2p, and so on. In Annie's case: 1p + 2p + 5p + 10p + 1p = 19p. Ask each pair to work out how much it costs to buy each of their names.

Word of the week

centimetre

Sample tasks
- Use your 10 cm strip to find an object which is about 10 centimetres long.
- How many centimetres long is your little finger?
- Draw a straight line which is about 4 centimetres long.

Sample facts
- a centimetre is a unit for measuring length or height
- 100 centimetres is the same length as 1 metre
- 'cm' is shorthand for centimetre
- 'cent' means 100, as in 'century', 'centipede'

N5 Subtraction

Round the class

Counting back in ones

Cubes

Point to a child and say a number, e.g. *twenty-eight*. That child has to respond by saying the number that is one less, e.g. *twenty-seven*. They choose another child (boys choose girls and vice versa), who has to say the number that is one less again, e.g. *twenty-six*. Continue until a child says *zero* or *nothing*. They take a cube. Start again with another number, e.g. 14, and another child. Who takes a cube this time?

twenty -seven

Imagine...

Taking away from a number up to 10

Tell the children to shut their eyes and imagine that they have five cakes. Choose a child to tell you about hers, e.g. *I have five chocolate cakes*. Choose another child to tell you about his. The children continue to keep their eyes shut. Now tell them that you are going to eat two of their biscuits. How many do they have now? The children write their suggestions on a piece of paper that they keep hidden. When you say, *Go!*, the children can show you the numbers they have written. Check their answers.

Rehearse how we take away 2 from 5 using fingers. Who was correct?

Number of the week

12

Sample tasks
- Count in twos to and beyond our number.
- Add 10, 20, 30, ... to our number.
- How many tens and units in our number?
- Say a pair which add to make our number, e.g. 6 and 6.
- Its tens digit is 1 less than its units digit. What other numbers are like this, e.g. 34?

Sample facts
- it is 2 more than 10, 3 more than 9
- it is between 10 and 15, but just nearer to 10
- it is 10 less than 22, 20 less than 32
- it is double 6
- 12 objects are called a dozen
- it is the number of months in a year

N6 Addition

Teddy pass

Counting in tens

A teddy bear

Give the teddy to one child, saying a 1-digit number, e.g. *eight*. They take the teddy and pass it to another child, saying the number ten more,
e.g. *eighteen*. That child passes the teddy on to another child, saying the number ten more, e.g. *twenty-eight*.
Keep passing the teddy like this.

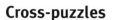

Cross-puzzles

Counting, adding

Draw a cross shape on the board.
Ask the children to copy it.
Tell them that you are going to give them clues for what goes in each space. Can they build up the whole cross?

clue for a: the number two more than 25
clue for b: double 10
clue for c: one less than 48.
clue for d: the number of days in January
clue for e: the number after 50.
Ask the children to write the signs to make the cross work.

Shape of the week

triangle

Sample tasks
- it is a flat shape
- it has 3 straight sides
- it has 3 corners
- it has 1 less side than a rectangle
- if you draw the diagonals of a rectangle, you make 2 triangles

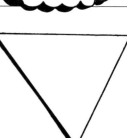

N7 Numbers to 100

Show me

Two more

Number cards (0 to 9), one set per pair
Ask the children to work together to show you the card number that is
two more than 8; then 12; then 6; then 2; then 18; then 20; then 14;
then 22; then 10. For example, when you say *eight*, they show you the 1
card and the 0 card held together to make 10.

Round the class

Counting in twos

Cubes
Point to a child and say a number, e.g. *fourteen*.
That child has to respond by saying the number that is two more, e.g.
sixteen. They choose another child (boys choose girls and vice versa), who
has to say the number that is two more again, e.g. *eighteen*.
Continue until a child says a number ending in 0, e.g. *twenty*. They take a
cube. Continue until a child says the next multiple of 10: *thirty*. That
child takes a cube. Keep going up to 50.
Repeat for a new starting number. Who takes a cube this time?

Number of the week

18

Sample tasks
- Count in twos forwards to our number, and backwards
  from our number.
- How many less than 20 is our number?
- Add 10, 20, ... to our number.
- Say a pair which add to our number, e.g. 8 and 10.
- How much change from 20p when you spend 18p?

Sample facts
- it is in the twos – the ninth two
- it is double 9
- it is made up of 1 ten and 8 units
- it is between 10 and 20, but much nearer 20
- it has a digit difference of 7, and a digit total of 9

N8 Number patterns

Imagine...

Doubling

Tell the children to shut their eyes and imagine that they have three cakes. Choose a child to tell you about hers, e.g. *They are three chocolate cakes with cherries on top.* Choose another child to tell you about his. The children continue to keep their eyes shut. Now tell them that you are going to double the number they have. How many do they have now? Write their suggestions on the board. The children can open their eyes and look at the suggestions.

Rehearse how to double 3 using fingers. Which suggestion was correct?

Letter prices

Adding several 1-digit numbers

Write a child's name on the board. Choose a child to come and write a number sequence: e.g. 1, 3, 5, 7. Choose a different child to write each number below a letter, so that each letter in the

child's name has a number under it. Now add up all the numbers. What does the name total? Ask each pair to write a series of numbers of their own and find the total for each of their names if one number is written under each letter. They may need some help doing the addition.

Word of the week

Sample tasks
- Draw a line to divide this square in half.
- Fold this paper in half. This is one way of folding it in half. This is another.
- Draw a circle, and draw a line to cut it in half. What shape is each half?
- If I give Ann and Gary half each of this cake, who gets the larger half? Neither, each half is the same.
- What is half of 10p?

Sample facts
- when a shape is split into two equal parts, each part is called one half
- two halves make the whole you start with
- a square which is cut in half makes two rectangles, or it can make two triangles
- if double 3 is 6, then half of 6 is 3

N9 Ordering

Bingo

Adding 10, 11 or 9

Number cards (0 to 20)

Each pair writes three numbers between 10 and 30 on a
piece of paper and draws a circle round each one.
Shuffle the number cards and place them in a pile face
down. Choose a child, who takes a card and says that card number out
loud. Every pair adds 10 to the card number. If the answer is one of the
numbers on their page, they can cross it out.
The first pair to cross out their three numbers wins.
Repeat for adding 11 or 9.

⟨17⟩
⟨23⟩
⟨29⟩

Speed track

Recognising the larger and smaller of two numbers

| 23 32 | | 45 51 |

Flash cards

Write ten pairs of numbers on ten flash cards, e.g. 23 and 32, 45 and 51,
etc. Show each of the flash cards in turn to the children and ask them to
write down the larger number on each one.
Time the process and show the cards fairly quickly. Explain that it is a
race. *Next time we will see if we can beat our own best time.*
Check the answer for each card. How many did each child score?

Number of the week

35

Sample tasks
- Count in fives forwards to our number, and backwards from our number.
- How many tens and units in our number?
- What is 10 more/10 less than our number?
- How many more need to be added to make 50?
- Say a pair which add to make our number, e.g. 20 and 15, 34 and 1.
- What three coins will make 35p?

Sample facts
- it is in the fives – the seventh five
- it is exactly halfway between 30 and 40
- it is an odd number
- both its digits are odd – they are next-door (consecutive) odd numbers
- it is 5 more than 30, 5 less than 40

N10 Addition

Number lines

Addition pairs to 10

Write these numbers in a column on the left-hand side of the board: 5, 4, 7, 10, 8, 3, 6, 9, 2, 0, 1.

Then go down the list and choose different children to write alongside each number to make 10.

One wrong!

Adding two numbers up to 20

A number line and Blu-tack

Unpeg 15 from the number line and Blu-tack it on the board.

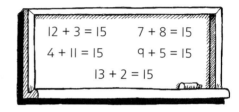

Write five addition pairs to 15 on the board.

Tell the children that one of the addition pairs is wrong.

Give them 3 or 4 minutes to work out which pair is wrong.

Then they can mark the teacher's work on the board, ticking the additions that are correct and putting a cross beside the one that is wrong.

Repeat for card 20.

Shape of the week

Sample tasks
- it is a flat shape
- it has four sides, all are the same length
- it has 4 corners
- a square piece of paper can be folded, then folded again, to make four smaller squares
- many everyday objects are square shaped
- it is the shape of the faces of a cube

N11 Money

Show me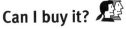

Taking away 9 or 10

Number cards (0 to 9), one set per pair

Ask the children to work together to show you the
number that is ten less than 13; then 17; then 16; then
11; then 18; then 12; then 19; then 14; then 20.
They do this by showing you the relevant card.
For example, when you say *thirteen*, they show you the 3 card.
Repeat for nine less.

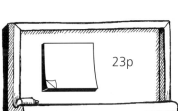

Can I buy it?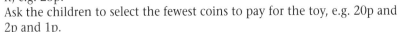

Using the fewest coins to make a total

1p, 2p, 5p, 10p and 20p coins

Tell the children you are selling a toy.
Make it something small, e.g. a pack
of stickers.

Draw it on the board. Put a price on
it, e.g. 23p.

23p

Ask the children to select the fewest coins to pay for the toy, e.g. 20p and
2p and 1p.

Discuss the different ways of making 23p.

Repeat for a new toy. Describe it and give it a different price. The children
have to use the fewest coins.

Number of the week

(16)

Sample tasks
- Count in twos forwards to our number, and backwards
  from our number.
- Which number doubled makes our number?
- Is it nearer to 10 or to 20? How near?
- Say a pair which add to make our number.
- What three coins will make 16p exactly?

Sample facts
- it is in the twos – the eighth two
- it is double 8
- its digits differ by 5, and total 7
- it is 6 more than 10, and 4 less than 20
- it has one odd and one even digit

(N12) Multiplication

Speed track

Doubling

Flash cards

Write ten numbers on ten flash cards, e.g. 2, 6, 9, 3, 8, 4, 7, 10, 5, 1. Write ten doubles at random on the board. Show each of the flash cards in turn to the children and ask them to write down the double of each one.

Time the process and show the cards fairly quickly. Explain that it is a race. *Next time we will see if we can beat our own best time.*
Check the answers for each card. How many did each child score?

Round the class

Counting in twos

Cubes

Point to a child and say a number, e.g. *fourteen*. That child has to respond by saying the number that is two more, e.g. *sixteen*. They choose another child (boys choose girls and vice versa), who has to say the number that is two more again, e.g. *eighteen*. Continue until a child says a number ending in 0, e.g. *twenty*. They take a cube. Continue like this until a child says the next multiple of ten: *thirty*. That child takes a cube. Keep going up to 50. Repeat for a new starting number. Who takes a cube this time?

Word of the week

Sample tasks
- How many 10 centimetre sticks measure the same length as one metre?
- Use the metre stick to find an object which is about 1 metre long.
- Look at the length of this table. Do you think it is more or less than 1 metre long?
- How many metres tall am I?

Sample facts
- a metre is a unit for measuring length or height
- metres are used to measure long lengths, centimetres are used for smaller lengths
- 1 metre is the same length as 100 centimetres
- a metre stick is used to measure lengths in metres

N13 Multiplication

Bingo

Multiplying by 2

Number cards (1 to 10)

Each pair writes three even numbers between 2 and 20 on a piece of paper and draws a circle round each one. Shuffle the number cards and place them in a pile face down. Choose a child, who takes a card and says that card number out loud. Every pair multiplies the card number by 2. If the answer is one of the numbers on their page, they can cross it out. The first pair to cross out their three numbers wins.

Cross-puzzles

Counting and multiplying

Draw a cross shape on the board and ask the children to copy it. Tell them that you are going to give them clues for what goes in each space. Can they build up the whole cross?

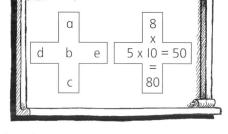

clue for a: double 4
clue for b: the number two more than 8
clue for c: one more than 79.
clue for d: the number on the smallest silver coin
clue for e: the number before 51.
Ask the children to write the signs to make the cross work.

Number of the week

Sample tasks
- Count in tens to our number, and beyond it.
- Count in fives forwards to our number, and backwards from our number
- Say a pair of tens which add to make our number, e.g. 10 and 40.
- How many of our number make 100, 200, ...?
- Add 10, 30, 20, 50, ... to our number.

Sample facts
- it is in the tens – the fifth ten – it is five tens
- it is in the fives – the tenth five – it is ten fives
- it is half of one hundred
- 100 is a century – 50 is half a century
- It is exactly halfway between 0 and 100

(N14) Fractions

Missing numbers

Counting in twos

Write a sequence of numbers on the board.

6, 8, 10, 12, 16, 18, 20, 22

Explain to the children that the numbers go up in twos, but that there is one missing.

Give them 3 or 4 minutes to discover the missing number.

Count in unison along the numbers on the board. Who wrote the correct number?

Play again, writing a new series of numbers: 3, 5, 7, 9, 13, 15, 17, 21, 23, 25, 27, 29 ... This time there are two missing numbers.

Story maths

Totals and change

1p, 2p, 5p, 10p, 20p and 50p coins

Tell the children a brief story. *One day, Renn went out shopping. She bought a pencil, a rubber and a sharpener. The pencil and the rubber were the same price, and the sharpener was 10p more. She gave the shopkeeper 50p and got 10p change. How much were each of the things she bought?*

Take suggestions and then use real coins to demonstrate the answer.

Tell another similar story.

Shape of the week

Sample facts
- a cuboid is a solid (3-d) shape
- it is the shape of most boxes
- it has 6 faces, which are either squares or rectangles
- it has 8 corners
- it has 12 edges

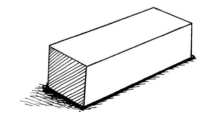

(N15) Numbers to 100

Letter prices

Counting in tens

Write the alphabet on the board.
Write 10p under a, 20p under b, 30p
under c, 10p under d, 20p under e, etc.
Ask each pair to work out how much it
would cost to buy their initials.

a	b	c	d	e
10p	20p	30p	10p	20p

f	g	h	i	j
30p	10p	20p	30p	10p

Teddy pass

Counting in fives

A teddy bear

Give the teddy to one child, saying, *five*.
They take the teddy and pass it to another child, saying the number five
more than you said.
That child passes the teddy on to another child, saying the number five
more.
Keep passing the teddy like this and counting in fives until you reach
100.
Start at 50 and count back in fives, passing the teddy each time.

Number of the week

Sample tasks
- Count in twos forwards to our number, and backwards
  from our number.
- How many tens and how many units in our number?
- Add 10, 20, ... to our number.
- Take 10, 20 from our number.
- What double makes our number (i.e. what is half our
  number?)

Sample facts
- it is in the twos – the twelfth two
- it is 4 more than 20
- it is between 20 and 30, but just nearer to 20
- it is two 12s, or two dozen
- it is the number of months in two years

(N16) Place-value

Two wrong!
Addition pairs to 8
A number line and Blu-tack
Unpeg 8 from the number line and Blu-tack it on the board. Write seven addition pairs to 8 on the board. Tell the children that two of these addition pairs are wrong. Give them 3 or 4 minutes to work out which pairs are wrong. Then they can mark the teacher's work on the board, ticking the sums that are correct and putting a cross beside those that are wrong.

Stick there
Tens and units
A dice and cubes
Put the children into two teams. Write *T* and *U* on the board for each team. The children take turns to throw the dice for their team. They write the number they have thrown on the

board in either the tens or the units column for their team, trying to make the largest number possible.

When each team has written two digits on the board, they all read the 2-digit number they have created.

Compare numbers. Which is the larger? That team gets a cube.

Play until one team has seven cubes.

Shape of the week

{ **pyramid** }

Sample tasks
- a pyramid has a pointed top or peak
- it has a bottom (base) on which it stands
- a pyramid's bottom (base) can be different shapes, e.g. a square, a triangle
- it has sloping faces which are triangles
- a pyramid with a square bottom has 5 faces – 1 square and 4 triangles

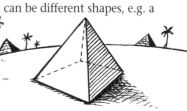

Missing numbers

Addition pairs to 9
Write a series of additions on
the board.
Explain to the children that
these are the different pairs of
numbers which make 9, but
one of the pairs is missing.

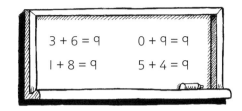

$$3 + 6 = 9 \qquad 0 + 9 = 9$$
$$1 + 8 = 9 \qquad 5 + 4 = 9$$

Give them 3 or 4 minutes to discover the missing addition pair.
Repeat for adding to 8.

Number lines

Doubling
Write on the board *Double this makes ?*
Then write these numbers in a column on the left-hand side of the board:
5, 4, 7, 10, 8, 3, 6, 9, 2, 20, 11.
Go down the list and choose different children to double each number
and write the answer beside it.

Number of the week

Sample tasks
- Count in ones forwards to and backwards from our
  number.
- Count in threes to and beyond our number.
- Count in tens from our number: 9, 19, 29, ...
- Say the odd numbers, in order from 1 to our number, and
  beyond.
- Say a pair of numbers which add to our number. How
  many are there?
- Add 10, 40, 70, ... to our number.

Sample facts
- it is 0 + 9, 1 + 8, 2 + 7
- it is 1 less than 10, 11 less than 20
- it is the fourth odd number
- its double is 18 – it is half of 18
- it is 1 more than the number of sides of an octagon

Addition

Bingo

Totals

1p, 2p, 5p and 10p coins

Each pair of children writes three amounts between 3p and 30p on a piece of paper and draws a circle round each one. Place three of each coin, 1p, 2p, 5p, 10p, in a cloth bag. Choose a child to take three or four coins, and to say which coins they have taken.

Each pair adds the coins to make a total. If the answer is one of the numbers on their page, they can cross it out. The first pair to cross out all their numbers wins.

(3p)
(9p)
(16p)

Show me

Addition pairs to ten

Number cards (0 to 9), one set per pair

Ask the children to show you the number which makes 10 if added to 3; then 7; then 6; then 1; then 8; then 2; then 9; then 4; then 5; then 10. For example, when you say *three*, they show you the *7* card. How fast can they do this?

Word of the week

even number

Sample tasks
- Say the first five even numbers.
- Say even or odd to these numbers: 4, 11, 9, 14, ... even, odd, odd, even, ...
- What is the next even number after 13, 38, 70, ...?
- How many even numbers are there between 30 and 50?

Sample facts
- the first even number is 2
- numbers which are not even are odd numbers
- even numbers have a units digit of 0, 2, 4, 6 or 8
- the 'twos' are all even, so are the 'tens'

N19 Subtraction

Imagine...

Taking away 1

Tell the children to shut their eyes and imagine that they have six toy figures (e.g. soldiers, dancers, animals, superheroes). Choose a child to tell you about hers, e.g. *They are six toy hedgehogs*. Choose another child to tell you about his. The children keep their eyes shut. Now tell them that you are going to take one toy away from them. How many do they have now? Write their suggestions on the board. The children can look at the suggestions.

Rehearse how to take away 1 from 6 using fingers. Who was correct? Repeat for a different number and taking away 2.

Round the class

Counting back in tens

Cubes

Point to a child and say a number, e.g. *ninety-eight*. That child has to respond by saying the number that is ten less, e.g. *eighty-eight*. They choose another child (boys choose girls and vice versa), who has to say the number that is ten less again, e.g. *seventy-eight*. Keep going until a child says a 1-digit number, e.g. *eight*. They take a cube. Start again with another number, e.g. 94, and another child. Who takes a cube this time?

Number of the week

Sample tasks
- Count in tens to and from our number.
- Count in fives to and from our number.
- Count in threes to our number.
- Take our number away from 35, 39, 42, ...
- Add our number to 12, 24, 58, ...
- Say a pair of tens which differ by our number, e.g. 20 and 50.

Sample facts
- it is in the tens – the third ten
- it is in the fives – the sixth five
- it is double 15, and half of 60
- it is the number of months in September, April, June, November
- it is exactly halfway between 20 and 40, 10 and 50

Numbers to 100

Cross-puzzles

Adding and subtracting

Draw a cross shape on the board and ask the children to copy it. Tell them that you are going to give them clues for what goes in each space. Can they build up the whole cross?

clue for a: the number 20 more than 25
clue for b: double 5
clue for c: five less than 60.
clue for d: the total if you add 50 and 55
clue for e: the number after 94.

Now ask the children to fill in the signs to make the cross work.

Speed track

Adding 3

Flash cards

Write ten additions on ten flash cards. Write ten answers at random on the board. Show each of the flash cards in turn to the children and ask them to write down the answer to each one. Time the process and show the cards fairly quickly. Explain that it is a race. *Next time we will see if we can beat our own best time.*

Then rehearse the answers to each card. How many did each child score?

Shape of the week

Sample facts
- it is a flat shape
- it has 4 straight sides – two longer equal sides and two shorter equal sides
- it has 4 corners
- it is the most common shape around us
- it is the shape of the faces of a cuboid
- it can be folded in half, then in half again to show 4 smaller rectangles

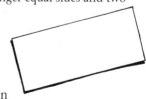

🔵N21 Addition/subtraction

Story maths

Coin recognition

5p, 10p, 20p and 50p coins

Tell the children a brief story. *Once upon a time there was a very clever cat called Carter. One day Carter was out prowling around when he found a little velvet purse. He realised that it was special because it contained coins of only one colour. The money in it added up to one pound and seventy pence, and there were two of each type of coin. What were the coins?* Take suggestions and then use real coins to demonstrate the answer. Tell another similar story.

Teddy pass

Counting in twenties

A teddy bear

Give the teddy to one child, saying a 1-digit number, e.g. *eight*. They take the teddy and pass it to another child, saying the number twenty more, e.g. *twenty-eight*. That child passes the teddy on to another child, saying the number twenty more, e.g. *forty-eight*. Keep passing the teddy like this. Go as far as you can, then start again with another 1-digit number.

Number of the week

3

Sample tasks
- Count in threes from our number to 30, and back.
- Add our number to 5, to 10, to 8, ...
- Take our number from 7, from 10, from 33, ...
- What is double our number?
- What must be added to our number to make 10, 20, 100, ...?

Sample facts
- it is the second odd number
- it is half of 6
- it is the number of sides of a triangle
- it is the number of months in a season
- it is 10 less than 13, 20 less than 23
- it is the number of letters in the words: one, six, ten

N22 Place-value

Which team?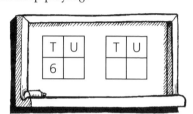

Tens and units

Place-value cards and cubes

Each pair chooses a tens card, e.g. 30.

Shuffle the units cards and place them in a pile face down.

Take a card from the pile and say it out loud, e.g. *five*.

Each pair combines that card with their tens card and creates a 2-digit number, which they write down.

If their number is a multiple of 11, e.g. 33, they may take a cube.

Take another units card from the pile and keep playing.

Stick there

Tens and units

Two dice and cubes

Put the children into two teams.

Write *T* and *U* on the board for each team.

The children take turns to throw the dice for their team.

They write the number they have thrown on the board in either the tens or the units column for their team, trying to make the largest number possible.

When each team has written two digits on the board, they all read the 2-digit number they have created.

Compare numbers. Which is the larger? That team gets a cube.

Play until one team has seven cubes.

Shape of the week

Sample facts
- it has a pointed top
- it has a bottom which is shaped like a circle
- it has a curved face
- it rolls on its curved face
- it is like a pyramid with a circle (circular) bottom
- cones are all around us, e.g. traffic cones, ice-cream cones

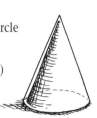

N23 Addition

Two wrong!

Addition pairs to 20

A number line and Blu-tack

Unpeg 20 from the number line and Blu-tack it on the
board. Write seven addition pairs to 20 on the board.
Tell the children that two of these addition pairs are wrong.
Give them 3 or 4 minutes to work out which pairs are
wrong. Then they can mark the teacher's work on the board, ticking the
additions that are correct and putting a cross beside those that are wrong.

Letter prices

Totals

Write 1p, 2p, 5p, 10p, 20p and
50p on the board.

Ask each pair to work out how
much it costs to buy each of
their names if the first letter

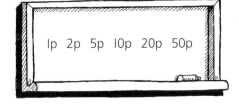

costs 1p, the second costs 2p, the third costs 5p and so on.
If their name has more than six letters, the seventh letter costs 1p, the
eighth costs 2p, the ninth costs 5p and so on.

Number of the week

Sample task
- Say the odd numbers, in order, to our number, and back.
- How many tens and how many units in our number?
- What must be added to our number to make 20?
- Add 7, 10, 4, ... to our number.
- Say a pair of numbers which add to our number, e.g. 14 and 3.
- What 3 coins make 17p?

Sample facts
- it is an odd number – the ninth odd number
- its digits are both odd
- its digits differ by 6 and total 8 – both these numbers are even
- it is between 10 and 20, but nearer to 20
- it is 83 less than 100

(N24) Subtraction

Number lines

Adding 10

Write on the board *This and 10 makes?*
Write these numbers in a column on the
left-hand side of the board: 5, 4, 7, 10, 8,
3, 6, 9, 2, 0, 1. Then go down the list and
choose different children to write the
result of adding 10.

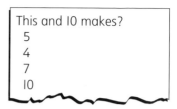

This and 10 makes?
5
4
7
10

Bingo

Adding 10, 11 or 9

Number cards (1 to 9), two sets

Each pair of children writes three numbers between 10 and 20 on a piece
of paper and draws a circle round each one. Shuffle the two sets of
number cards and place them in a pile face down. Choose a child, who
takes a card and says that number out loud. Every pair adds 10 to the card
number. If the answer is one of the numbers on their page, they can cross
it out. The first pair to cross out their three numbers wins.
Repeat for adding 11 or 9.

Word of the week

Sample tasks
- Draw lines to divide this square into quarters.
- Fold this paper in quarters.
- Draw a circle, and draw two lines to cut it in quarters.
  What shape is each quarter?
- If I give Kirstie, Glenn, Corin and Chris a quarter each of
  this cake, who gets the larger quarter? Neither, each
  quarter is the same.
- What is a quarter of 8p?

Sample facts
- when a shape is split into four equal parts, each part is
  called one quarter
- four quarters make the whole you start with
- two quarters make one half
- a square which is cut in quarters makes four smaller
  squares, or it can make four triangles

N25 Multiplication

Cross-puzzles

Adding and subtracting

Draw a cross shape on the board
and ask the children to copy it.
Tell them that you are going to
give them clues for what goes in
each space. Can they build up
the whole cross?

clue for a: ten more than 7

clue for b: double 4

clue for c: two less than 11.

clue for d: the total number of fingers and thumbs on three hands

clue for e: double 11 and add 1.

Now ask the children to fill in the signs to make the cross work.

```
        a               17
                        –
d   b   e       15 + 8 = 23
                        =
        c               q
```

Speed track

Multiplying by 5

Flash cards

Write ten calculations on ten flash cards, e.g. $4 \times 5 =$, $6 \times 5 =$, $2 \times 5 =$,
$7 \times 5 =$, etc. Write ten answers at random on the board.

Show each of the flash cards in turn to the children and ask them to write
down the answer to each one. Time the process and show the cards fairly
quickly. Explain that it is a race. *Next time we will see if we can beat our own
best time.* Then rehearse the answers to each card. How many did each
child score?

Number of the week

Sample tasks
- Count in fives from our number.
- Count in tens from our number.
- Add 30, 70, 120, ... to our number.
- What is double our number?
- How many of our number make 20, 35, 50, ...?

Sample facts
- it is half of 10
- it is the digit total of 14, 23, 41, 32, 50
- it is the number of 20p coins which make £1
- it is the number of toes on a foot
- it is the number of sides of a pentagon
- it is the number of letters in the numbers; three,
  seven, eight

N26 Division

Missing numbers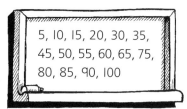

Counting in fives

Write a sequence of numbers on the board.
Explain to the children that the numbers go up in fives, but that there are four missing. Give them 3 or 4 minutes to discover the missing numbers.

5, 10, 15, 20, 30, 35, 45, 50, 55, 60, 65, 75, 80, 85, 90, 100

Round the class

Counting in tens

Cubes

Point to a child and say a number, e.g. *forty-three*. That child has to respond by saying the number that is ten more, e.g. *fifty-three*.

They choose another child (boys choose girls and vice versa), who has to say the number that is ten more again, e.g. *sixty-three*. Keep going until a child says a number with a 9 in it, e.g. 93. They take a cube. Continue like this until you pass 200, giving a cube every time a child says a number with a 9 in it.
Start again with a different number, e.g. 58. Who takes a cube this time?

Shape of the week

cylinder

Sample tasks
- a cylinder is a hollow or solid shape (3-d)
- it has two identical circle (circular) ends
- a solid cylinder has a curved face and 2 flat circle faces
- it rolls
- cylinders are around us, e.g. tins, pipes, bins

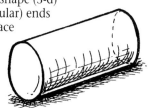

N27 Fractions

Story maths

Taking away from a number up to 20

Number grid

Tell the children a brief story. *Three children went out together to buy a computer game for £20. One child had £20, one had £18 and one had £15. It was a very windy day, and the wind blew away £5 from each child. Did they have enough money left between them to buy their computer game?*

Take suggestions and use the number grid to demonstrate the answer. Tell another, similar story.

Teddy pass

Counting back in fives

A teddy bear and number grid

Give the teddy to one child, saying a number, e.g. *eighty*. They take the teddy and pass it to another child, saying the number five less, e.g. *seventy-five*.

That child passes the teddy on to another child, saying the number five less, e.g. *seventy*.

Keep passing the teddy like this. The children may need a number grid to help them.

Number of the week

2

Sample tasks
- Say the even numbers starting with our number.
- Count in tens from our number.
- How many 2p coins make 8p, 12p, 6p, ...?
- Take our number away from 21, 32, 40, ...
- Add our number to 19, 99, 69, ...

Sample facts
- it is the first even number
- it is the number in a pair
- it is the difference between two next-door odd numbers, and two next-door even numbers
- it makes 10 with 8, 20 with 18, 30 with 28
- it is the number of days in a weekend

N28 Numbers to 100

Bingo

Taking away 10, 11 or 9

Number cards (10 to 100)

Each pair of children writes five numbers between 10 and
100 on a piece of paper and draws a circle round each one.
Shuffle the number cards and place them in a pile face
down.

Choose a child, who takes a card and says that number out loud.
All the children, in unison, subtract 10 and say the answer.
If the answer matches one of the numbers on their page, they can cross
it out.
The first pair to cross out two of their five numbers wins.
Repeat for subtracting 9 or 11.

How many?

Estimating and counting to 100

Take a book with about 45–55 pages and show it to the children. Flick
through the pages. Ask the children to write down how many pages they
think there are.

When everyone has written down an estimate, choose a child to help
count.

Count the pages in fives, making a mark on the board after each five.
Finally count the marks: *five, ten, fifteen, twenty.* Whose estimate was
closest?

Word of the week

second (time)

Sample tasks
- Use the stopclock to say 'stop' together when 10 seconds
  have passed.
- Use the stopclock to count the seconds in tens for one
  minute.
- Guess 10 seconds without looking at the stopclock.
- How many seconds are there in half a minute?

Sample facts
- a second is a small period of time
- there are 60 seconds in 1 minute
- a quarter of a minute is 15 seconds

N29 Ordering

Three wrong!

Adding two numbers (crossing 10)
Write eight additions on the board.
Tell the children that three of these additions are wrong.
Give the children 3 or 4 minutes to work out which are the wrong additions.

8 + 2 = 10	8 + 3 = 11
6 + 4 = 10	6 + 5 = 12
7 + 3 = 10	7 + 4 = 13
9 + 4 = 12	9 + 6 = 15

Then they can mark the teacher's work on the board, ticking those additions that are correct and putting a cross beside those that are wrong.

Letter prices

Totals
Write the alphabet on the board.
Then write 1p, 2p, 5p and 10p under the first four letters, the same amounts under the next four and so on.
Ask each pair to construct a word that costs exactly 20p.
They can also work out the cost of their names.

Number of the week

15

Sample tasks
- Say the odd numbers from 1 to our number, and beyond.
- Count in threes to our number, and beyond.
- Count in fives to our number, and beyond.
- Say two numbers which add to our number, e.g. 10 and 5.
- Say three numbers which add to our number, e.g. 4, 5 and 6.

Sample facts
- it is an odd number – the eighth odd number
- it is in the threes and in the fives
- it is exactly halfway between 10 and 20
- it makes 20 with 5, 50 with 35, 100 with 85
- it is 1 more than the number of days in 2 weeks

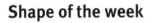 Addition

Number lines

Addition pairs to 20

Write on the board *This and what makes 20?*

Then write these numbers in a column on the left-hand side of the board:
5, 4, 7, 10, 8, 3, 6, 9, 2, 0, 1.

Go down the list and choose different children to write alongside each the number that adds to it to make 20.

The children can check their own answers.

Show me

Adding three 1-digit numbers

Number cards (0 to 9), one set per pair, plus three

Shuffle three more sets of cards and place them in a pile face down.

Take two cards and hold them up.

Ask a child to add them, then write the total on the board.

Ask the children to hold up the number that goes with that total to make 20.

Shape of the week

(pentagon)

Sample tasks
- a pentagon is a flat shape (2-d)
- it has 5 straight sides
- it has 5 corners
- its sides are sometimes all the same length (regular pentagon), and sometimes not
- it has 1 more side than a square or rectangle
- you can join some of its corners to make 3 triangles inside

Imagine...

Addition pairs to 10

Tell the children to shut their eyes and imagine that they have ten fingers with a finger puppet on each one standing in front of them.

Choose a child to tell you about hers, e.g. *The finger puppets are mice with long whiskers.* Now tell them that you are going to fold down four fingers. How many are still standing up now? Write their suggestions on the board. The children can open their eyes and look at the suggestions. Rehearse how to find the pairs that make 10 using fingers.

Cross-puzzles

Adding and subtracting

Draw a cross shape on the board and ask the children to copy it. Tell them that you are going to give them clues for what goes in each space. Can they build up the whole cross?

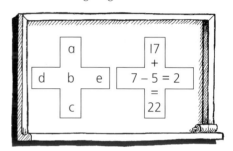

clue for a: the amount which is 3p less than 20p

clue for b: the smallest silver coin

clue for c: counting in twos, the number after 20.

clue for d: the total amount if you have 2p and 5p in your purse

clue for e: the largest bronze coin.

Now ask the children to fill in the signs to make the cross work.

Number of the week

20

Sample tasks
- Count in twos to and from our number.
- Count in fives to and from our number.
- Count in twenties starting with our number.
- What must be added to 15, 7, 13, 2, ... to make our number?
- What is 5 more, 17 more, 40 more, ... than our number?
- How many 20p coins make 60p, £1, £2, ...?

Sample facts
- it is the tenth even number
- it is double 10, and half of 40
- it is in the fives – the fourth five – the number of toes on 4 feet
- it is called a 'score'
- it is 2×10, 4×5

N32 Addition

Story maths

Coin recognition

Tell the children a brief story. *Once upon a time, a clever owl was unable to sleep. To help himself fall asleep, he started to count. But this was boring, so after a while he invented a*

little game. He counted and added. He started at 1, and added 2, and then added 3, and then added 4, and then added 5. How far did he get if his total was over 30?

Give each pair a short while to work on the problem, and then go through it.

Bingo

Doubling

Number cards (1 to 10), two sets

Each pair of children writes six even numbers between 2 and 20 on a piece of paper and draws a circle round each one.

Shuffle two sets of number cards and place them in a pile face down.

Choose a child, who takes a card and says that number out loud.

Every pair doubles the card number.

If the answer is one of the numbers on their page, they can cross it out.

The first pair to cross out their six numbers wins.

Shape of the week

sphere

Sample facts
- a sphere is a solid or hollow shape (3-d)
- it is the name for the shape of a ball
- it has 1 curved face
- many objects are shaped like a sphere, e.g. marble, globe, ball
- it rolls

ⓝ³³ Addition/subtraction

Speed track

Taking away to a multiple of 10

Flash cards

Write ten subtractions on ten flash cards, e.g.
13 − 3 = , 27 − 7 = , 16 − 6 = , 41 − 1 = , etc.
(The answers should all be multiples of ten.)
Show each of the flash cards in turn to the
children and ask them to write down the answer to each one.
Time the process and show the cards fairly quickly. Explain that it is a
race. *Next time we will see if we can beat our own best time.*
Then rehearse the answers to each card. How many did each child score?

| 13 − 3 = | 27 − 7 = |
| 16 − 6 = | 41 − 1 = |

Show me

Difference

Number cards (1 to 10), one set per pair

Ask the children to show you the number that is the difference between:
3 and 7; then 6 and 11; then 4 and 14; then 8 and 12; then 9 and 15;
then 7 and 13; then 14 and 18; then 15 and 21.

For example, when you say *The difference between 3 and 7 is?*, they show
you the 4 card. Keep going like this through different pairs.

Number of the week

Sample tasks
- Say the odd numbers, starting with our number.
- Count in tens from our number.
- Take our number from 40, 100, 38, 110, ...
- Say a number whose digit difference is our number, e.g. 43.
- Double our number (2), then double the answer (4), and so on. How far can you go?

Sample facts
- it is the first odd number
- it makes 10 with 9, 20 with 19
- it is the difference between two next-door (consecutive) numbers
- it is the number of sides of a circle
- it is the difference between the number of sides of a pentagon and a square
- it is the number of letters in the shortest word – 'a'

Numbers to 1000

Teddy pass

Counting in ones

A teddy bear

Give the teddy to one child, saying a 3-digit number,
e.g. *one hundred and forty-six*.

They take the teddy and pass it to another child, saying
the number one more than you said, e.g. *one hundred
and forty-seven*. That child passes the teddy on to another child, saying
the number one more, e.g. *one hundred and forty-eight*.

Keep passing the teddy like this.

Missing numbers

Counting in ones, tens or hundreds

Write a series of numbers on the board.
Explain to the children that the numbers
go up in ones, but that there are three
missing. Give them 3 or 4 minutes to
discover the missing numbers.

389, 390, 391, 392, 394,
395, 396, 398, 399, 400,
401, 403, 404, 405

Repeat for sequences of tens or hundreds: 100, 200, 300, 500, 700.

Word of the week

difference

Sample tasks
- What is the difference between 5 and 2?
- What is the difference between the digits in the number 72?
- What is the difference in height between Chloe and Sam?
- If the difference between two numbers is 3, and one number is 10, what is the other?
- If a sticker costs 8p, and you pay with a 10p coin, what is the difference?

Sample facts
- the difference between two numbers is how much more one is than the other
- the difference between two numbers is how much less one is than the other
- to find the difference between two numbers you can take the smaller away from the larger
- to find the difference between two numbers you can count on from the smaller to the larger

N35 Doubling/halving

Letter prices

Counting in twos

Write the alphabet on the board.
Underneath the alphabet write the
amounts 2p, 4p, 6p, 8p, 10p.
Choose a child to come and write the
next amount (12p).

a	b	c	d	e
2p	4p	6p	8p	10p
f	g	h	i	j
12p	14p	16p	18p	20p

Choose a different child to write the next amount (14p).
Ask each pair to work out how much it costs to buy each of their initials.
They can then write a simple 3-letter word and work out the cost of this.

One wrong!

Doubling

Write ten numbers and their doubles on the board.
Tell the children that one of these doubles is wrong.
Give them 3 or 4 minutes to work out which it is.
Then they can mark the teacher's work on the board, ticking those that
are correct and putting a cross beside the one that is wrong.

Number of the week

Sample tasks
- Count in tens to and from our number. Repeat for twenties.
- Count in fives to and from our number.
- Say a number which has our number as its nearest 10, e.g. 38, 41.
- Say a pair of tens which differ by our number, e.g. 10 and 50.
- Halve our number, then halve again, and keep going.

Sample facts
- it is in the fives – the eighth five
- it is the fourth ten
- it is the nearest ten for 44, 36, 39
- it is double 20
- it is $4 \times 10, 8 \times 5$
- it is two twenties or two score

N36 Place-value

Round the class

Counting in tens

Cubes

Point to a child and say a 3-digit number, e.g. *three hundred and forty-eight*. That child has to respond by saying the number that is ten more, e.g. *three hundred and fifty-eight*. They choose another child (boys choose girls and vice versa), who has to say the number that is ten more again, e.g. *three hundred and sixty-eight*. Keep going until a child says a number with a 9 in it, e.g. 398. They take a cube. Continue as long as you can, giving a cube every time a child says a number with a 9 in it. Start again with another number, e.g. 254, and another child. Who takes a cube this time?

Which ticket?

Rounding to the nearest ten

Cubes

Tell the children to shut their eyes and imagine that they have raffle ticket. They should think very hard about what number is on their ticket. Ask them to open their eyes and write their number on a piece of paper, keeping it secret.

Now you say *ten*. Has anyone imagined a raffle ticket with a number on it that rounds to 10? Each child for whom that is true takes a cube.

Say another multiple of 10, e.g. *thirty*. Who has a number that rounds to 30? Each of those children takes a cube.

Keep going, saying multiples of 10 until everyone has a cube.

Shape of the week

Sample tasks
- it is a flat shape (2-d)
- it has 6 straight sides
- it has 6 corners
- its sides are sometimes all the same length (regular hexagon), and sometimes not
- 'hex' means 6
- hexagons of the same size fit together with no gaps
- you can join opposite corners of the hexagon to make 8 identical triangles

(N37) Addition/subtraction

Number lines

Addition pairs to 100

Write on the board *This and what makes 100?*

Then write these numbers in a column on the left-hand side of the board: 50, 40, 70, 10, 80, 30, 60, 90, 20, 0, 100.

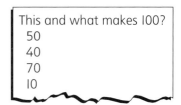

This and what makes 100?
50
40
70
10

Go down the list and choose different children to write the pair to make 100.

Story maths

Adding and subtracting

Tell the children a brief story. *One day, two squirrels were busy collecting nuts to store for winter time. One told the other that she had stored enough nuts that she could eat one a day for two weeks. The other said that she had ten more than that! How many nuts do they have between them? How many more do they each have to find to have 50?*

Give the children several minutes to work out the answers, then rehearse the calculation.

Tell another, similar story.

Number of the week

Sample tasks
- Count in twos to and from our number.
- Count in fours to and from our number.
- Say an addition which makes our number, e.g. 3 + 5 = 8.
- Say a subtraction from our number, e.g. 8 – 5 = 3.
- What is half our number? What is double our number?

Sample facts
- it is the fourth even number
- subtracting 2 from our number leaves 6
- it is the difference between 2 and 10, 12 and 20, 22 and 30, ...
- it is 8 × 1, 4 × 2, 2 × 4, 1 × 8
- it is the number of sides of an octagon

N38 Addition

Cross-puzzles

Adding and subtracting

Draw a cross shape on the board and ask the children to copy it. Tell them that you are going to give them clues for what goes in each space. Can they build up the whole cross?

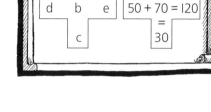

clue for a: two more than 98

clue for b: double 35

clue for c: two less than 32.

clue for d: the total number of fingers and thumbs on ten hands

clue for e: the number after 119.

Now ask the children to fill in the signs to make the cross work.

Teddy pass

Counting in tens

A teddy bear

Give the teddy to one child, saying a 3-digit number, e.g. *six hundred and thirty-five*. They take the teddy and pass it to another child, saying the number ten more, e.g. *six hundred and forty-five*.

That child passes the teddy on to another child, saying the number ten more, e.g. *six hundred and fifty-five*. Keep passing the teddy like this.

Word of the week

Sample tasks
- If we share 8 cakes between 4 people, what is the remainder?
- If 5 biscuits are shared between 2 people, how many do each get, and what is the remainder?
- If I share 10p between some children, between how many can I share it with no remainder?

Sample facts
- a remainder is what is left when objects have been shared equally
- if a set of objects will share equally, then there is no remainder
- odd numbers have a remainder of 1 when divided by 2
- '÷' is shorthand for 'divided by'

N39 Multiplication

Missing numbers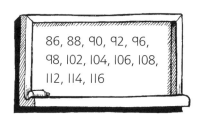

Counting in twos
Write a series of numbers on the board.
Explain to the children that the numbers go up in twos, but that there are three missing.
Give them 3 or 4 minutes to discover the missing numbers.

86, 88, 90, 92, 96,
98, 102, 104, 106, 108,
112, 114, 116

Number lines

Multiplying by 10
Write on the board *10 times this makes ?*
The write these numbers in a column on the left-hand side of the board:
5, 4, 7, 10, 8, 3, 6, 9, 2, 0, 11.
Go down the list and choose different children to write alongside each the number obtained by multiplying it by 10.

Number of the week

Sample tasks
- Count in twos to and from our number.
- Count in threes to and from our number.
- Say a pair which add to make our number.
- Say a pair of numbers which multiply to make our number, e.g. 6 × 2.
- What is our number divided by 2, by 3, by 4, by 6, by 12?

Sample facts
- it is the sixth even number
- it is 1 × 12, 2 × 6, 3 × 4, 4 × 3, 6 × 2, 12 × 1
- when 12p is shared between 4 people, each gets 3p, ...
- it is between 10 and 20
- its nearest ten is 10
- it is the number of hours in half a day

(N40) Division

Show me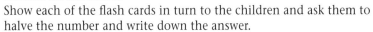

Adding 9 or 11

Number cards (11 to 20), one set per pair

Ask the children to show you the number that is eleven more than 3; then 7; then 6; then 1; then 8; then 2; then 9; then 4; then 5.
For example, when you say *three*, they show you the 14 card.
Repeat for nine more.

Speed track

Halving

Flash cards

Write ten numbers on ten flash cards, e.g. 24, 16, 30, 12, 22, 18, 40, 26, 8, 50.
Write the halves of these numbers at random on the board.

Show each of the flash cards in turn to the children and ask them to halve the number and write down the answer.
Time the process and show the cards fairly quickly. Explain that it is a race. *Next time we will see if we can beat our own best time.*
Rehearse the answers to each card. How many did each child score?

Shape of the week

{ octagon }

Sample facts
- it is a flat shape (2-d)
- it has 8 straight sides
- it has 8 corners
- 'oct' means 8, as in 'octopus'
- it has 2 more sides than a hexagon, and 3 more than a pentagon

N41 Fractions

Teddy pass

Counting in fours

A teddy bear

Give the teddy to one child, saying *four*.

They take the teddy and pass it to another child, saying the number four more, *eight*.

That child passes the teddy on to another child, saying the number four more, *twelve*. Keep passing the teddy like this.

Bingo

Adding

Number cards (5 to 15)

Each pair of children writes three numbers between 10 and 30 on a piece of paper and draws a circle round each one.

Shuffle the number cards and place them in a pile face down.

Choose a child, who takes two cards and says both numbers out loud.

Every pair adds the two numbers. Discuss how to do this and write the total on the board.

If the answer is one of the numbers on their page, they can cross it out. The first pair to cross out their three numbers wins.

Number of the week

Sample tasks
- Count in twos from our number.
- Count in fours from our number.
- Count in tens from our number.
- What is one half, one quarter of our number?
- What is 2×, 5×, 10× our number?

Sample facts
- it is the second even number
- it is the number of quarters in one whole
- it is the number of sides of a square and a rectangle
- it is the number of letters in 'four', 'five', nine'
- it is the difference between the number of sides of a square and an octagon

Activity Bank

The Activity Bank includes a variety of activities that address key skills. The activities in the bank can be used at any time alongside any topic, and often you will wish to revisit them throughout the year.

The table lists each activity in the bank, along with the key skill addressed, to help your selection.

Activity	Skill

Counting

Quiet and loud	Counting in ones
Silent counting	Counting in ones
Animal count-around	Counting in tens
Stand up, sit down	Counting in twos
Animal voices	Counting in fives

Place-value, ordering and comparing

Say and write	Tens and units
Largest digit	Hundreds, tens and units
Four in a row!	Ordering numbers up to 100
Nearest to mine!	Comparing numbers up to 100

Adding

Take a cube!	Addition pairs for numbers up to 10
Card hold-up	Addition pairs for numbers up to 10
Guess the card	Addition pairs to 10
Hand it over	Addition pairs to 10
Jump up!	Addition pairs to 20
Shout back!	Addition pairs to 20

Activity	Skill
Pair up	Addition pairs to 100
Point collector	Adding 10 to a 2-digit number
Match mine!	Adding multiples of ten
How much in all?	Addition: bridging through a multiple of ten
Find a partner	Doubling by adding
What's on the card?	Doubling by adding

Subtracting

Stand up!	One less
Grid roll-on	One less
Name count back	Counting back
Collect a cube	Missing numbers
Multiple nearby!	Missing numbers
Whose card?	Ten more or less
Multiple choice!	Subtracting multiples of ten

Money

Missing coin!	Coin recognition
Coins together	Coin recognition
Take the same!	Exchange
In my pocket	Totals
Buying cakes	Change

Multiplication and division

Team effort	×2 multiplication facts
Two of the fives!	×5 multiplication facts
Missing tens	×10 multiplication facts
Dice chances	Multiplication facts up to 6×6
Chains	Halving
Towering division	Dividing by grouping

Activity	Skill

Solving problems in real life and measures

I spy	Estimating lengths
Animal heights	Adding and subtracting lengths
Think of a length	Estimating lengths
Story time	Solving problems involving measures
More time	Solving problems involving time
Magrical Mystery Tour	Solving problems involving time
Hop timer	Solving problems involving time
Next day	Solving problems involving time
Next month	Knowing the months and their order

① Counting

Quiet and loud

Counting in ones

In unison, chant in ones, starting at a given number, e.g. twelve.

Point to a child, who stops counting – the remainder of the class continue.

Point to another child, then another, ... until only about five children are still counting.

Point to a child, who starts counting again. Point to another, then another, ... until the whole class are once more counting in unison.

Silent counting

Counting in ones

Cubes

Choose a child to stand at the front. Give them a number. They turn around and start counting from that number, quietly or silently. The rest of the class also count silently (they can count in pairs, mouthing the numbers to each other).

After a few moments, shout *Stop!*

Each child writes down the number they reached. Compare with the child at the front. The children who were closest each take a cube. Repeat with a different child at the front.

Animal count-around

Counting in tens

The children work in groups of four or five. Each group is designated by an animal which you draw or write on the board, e.g. cats, badgers, dogs, foxes, hares.

Start counting in unison in tens from a given number. Point to an animal, e.g. foxes. The 'foxes' take over counting in tens. Point to a different animal – that group now takes over the count. Continue around the groups.

Variation: Each group counts, then chooses the next group to take over.

Stand up, sit down

Counting in twos

Count in twos, in unison *Two, four, six, ...* After a short while, stop the count. Point to a child, who stands up and continues the count alone. Point to another child who stands up and begins counting. At the same time the first child stops counting and sits down. Continue like this around the class.

Practise over time so that the change-overs do not interrupt the count.

Animal voices

Counting in fives

Start counting in fives, in unison *Five, ten, fifteen, ...* Stop after three or four numbers. Point to a child who says the next number in the count in the voice of an animal, e.g. *Quack, quack, twenty.* Point to another child, who says the next number in the voice of a different animal, e.g. *Woof, woof, twenty-five.*

Keep a lively pace, so the children are not sure who you will point to next. How long can children keep the count going?

❷ Place-value, ordering and comparing

Say and write

Tens and units

Cubes

Choose a child who says a 2-digit number, e.g. *Forty-six*. Each child writes the number down. The first child chooses a second child to write the number on the board.

Check with the class, (assist, if necessary). Each child compares their written number with that on the board. Anyone whose number is correct takes a cube.

Repeat, starting with a different 2-digit number. It may help to have a number grid on display.

Largest digit

Hundreds, tens and units

Place-value cards (Hs, Ts, Us), cubes

Shuffle each set of cards separately and place them face down in three piles.

Divide the class into three teams: the Tens, the Units and the Hundreds. Choose a child from each team to take a card from the appropriate pile and read their number aloud.

The children place the three cards together and read aloud the new number.

Whose digit is largest? Hundreds, tens or units? That team collect a cube. Repeat, until all the cards have been used.

Four in a row!

Ordering numbers up to 100

Number cards (0 to 100), cubes

The children work in groups of three or four.

Deal four cards to each group. Each group arranges their cards in order from largest to smallest.

Call out *Largest*. Each group holds up their largest card. The group with the largest collects a cube.

Repeat for the largest of the three remaining cards.

Repeat twice more for the remaining cards.

Play again. After several rounds, which group has the most cubes?

Nearest to mine!

Comparing numbers up to 100

Place-value cards (Ts and Us), cubes

The children work in pairs.

Shuffle each set of cards separately and place them face down in two piles.

Each pair writes a 2-digit number on a piece of paper. Take a tens card and a units card to make a 2-digit number. Read it aloud, with the class.

All the pairs with a number larger than yours stand up. Check they are correct.

All the pairs with a number smaller than yours stand up. Check they are correct.

Agree with the class whose number is closest. That pair collect a cube. Repeat.

❸ Adding

Take a cube!

Addition pairs for numbers up to 10

Cubes

Write '7' on the board. Choose a child and say a number less than 7, e.g. *five*. That child responds with the addition pair to 7, i.e. *two*. If correct, that child collects a cube.

Continue around the class. Repeat for bonds to other numbers, e.g. 6, 8, 9.

Card hold-up

Addition pairs for numbers up to 10

Sets of number cards (0 to 9)

The children work in pairs, each with a set of number cards.

Write 9 on the board. Each pair chooses two cards that total 9, e.g. 4 and 5 (they should hide their cards from other children). Say *Show me!* Each pair holds up their cards, facing you. Choose different pairs to read out their numbers.

Repeat for other bonds for numbers up to 10 – keep up a lively pace.

Guess the card

Addition pairs to 10

Number cards (0 to 9)

Choose two children and give one of them the set of number cards. That child chooses a card (e.g. 7) and shows you and the other child, but no-one else. The second child says the bond to 10, i.e. *Three*.

The rest of the class have to guess the number on the card. Reveal the card. Were they correct? Choose different children and play again.

Hand it over

Addition pairs to 10

Sets of number cards (0 to 10)

The children work in pairs, each with a set of number cards.

The children sort their cards into pairs that make 10 (1 and 9, 4 and 6, etc.).

They select one pair and hold the cards, hidden from their neighbours.

Say a pair of numbers: *Six and four.* Any pair holding those cards can hand them over to you, and choose a new pair.

Continue for each bond to 10. Can any pair hand over all their cards (except 5)?

Jump up!

Addition pairs to 20

Sets of number cards (0 to 20)

Deal one card to each child. Say a number, up to 20, aloud, e.g. *seven*. All the children holding the card 7 jump up.

Allow the rest of the children a moment to decide if they are holding the pair to make 20

i.e. 13). Say *Ready, steady, jump!*

All the children holding 13 jump up. Check they are correct.

Write the bond on the board: 7 + 13 = 20.

Repeat for other numbers up to 20, until all the bonds have been recorded.

Shout back!

Addition pairs to 20

Number line (0 to 20)

Choose a group of about six children to stand up (e.g. all those with five letters in their name). Point to a number on the line, and read it aloud e.g. *Five*. The group shout back the number bond to 20, i.e. *Fifteen*.

Choose a child to write the addition on the board, 5 + 15 = 20.

Choose a new group (e.g. all those whose name begins with 'b') and repeat.

Continue for each pair to 20.

Pair up

Addition pairs to 100

Number cards (0, 10, 20, ... 100)

The children work in pairs. Each pair writes a pair of tens that total 100, e.g. 40 and 60, hidden from their neighbours.

Select a card at random, hold it up and read it aloud. Any pair with a bond including that number stand up. Choose a pair to read their bond aloud, and write it on the board.

Repeat for each card (note that each pair will have two chances to stand up).

Point collector

Adding 10 to a 2-digit number

Number grid (1 to 100), cubes

Each child writes 10 different numbers (up to 100) on a piece of paper. Point to a number at random on the grid, e.g. 41. Choose a child to add ten and say the answer aloud, i.e. *Fifty-one*. Any child with the matching number can cross it out and collect a cube.

Repeat, until one child has three cubes.

Match mine!

Adding multiples of ten

Number grid (1 to 100), a dice

The children work in pairs.

Point to a 2-digit number on the grid, say it together and write it on the board, e.g. 32. Each pair adds a multiple of ten to the number (from 10 to 60), and writes the appropriate addition, e.g. 32 + 40 = 72.

Throw the dice (e.g. 5) and add that many tens to the first number, writing it on the board.

32 + 50 = 82.

Any pair with the same addition scores a point.

Repeat.

How much in all?

Addition: bridging through a multiple of ten

A selection of coins

The children work in pairs.

Show the children an amount of money between 20p and 30p, e.g. 27p. *How much do I have?* Each pair writes down the amount. Tell them that in your pocket you have an extra amount, e.g. 4p. *What is the total?* (Ensure the addition bridges through a multiple of ten.) Take suggestions for the total, then work through the addition on the board, encouraging the strategy of first adding to make the next ten, i.e. 27 + 3 + 1. Repeat for other totals, e.g. 28 + 3, 17 + 5, 26 + 6.

Find a partner

Doubling by adding

Sets of number cards (1 to 20)

Deal one card to each child. Any child with a number up to 10 has to find a partner with double that number. Any child with a number between 10 and 20 has to find a partner with half that number. Allow a few minutes – there will be some children without a partner (e.g. 17). There will be some children in groups of three (e.g. 4, 8, 16). Discuss the results and record them on the board.

What's on the card?

Doubling by adding

Number cards (1 to 10)

Choose a child to stand at the front and give them a card, hidden from the class. That child doubles the number and says the answer aloud.

Choose different children to suggest what they think the number on the card is, and write some guesses on the board. Ask the first child to reveal the card. Who was correct?

Repeat with a different child.

④ Subtracting

Stand up!

One less

Sets of number cards (1 to 20), a teddy or other soft toy

Deal one card to each child. Give one child the teddy. They stand up and read their number aloud. Any child with the number one less stands up and reads their number aloud. If correct one of them chooses another child, who is given the teddy. They stand up and read their number aloud. Again, any child with the number one less stands up and reads their number aloud.
Continue.

eleven.

Grid roll-on

One less

Number grid (1 to 100), 2p coin

Place the grid flat on the floor. Choose a child to roll the coin onto the grid. Write the number where it lands on the board, and read it together with the class. Choose a child to say the number one less. If correct, that child rolls the coin to find a new starting number.

Variation: This activity is easily adapted for 'ten less'.

Name count back

Counting back

Write 20 on the board. Each child calculates how many letters are in their name, and counts back that number from 20, writing the number they finish on (e.g. Matthew will finish on 13 – remembering not to start on 20). Point to 20 and, together, count back one. *Does anyone have 19? No, because no-one has a one-letter name.*

Point to 20 and, together, count back two. *Does anyone have 18?*
Repeat, counting back three, four, five, …

Collect a cube

Missing numbers

Sets of number cards (1 to 10)

Deal one card to each child.
Write an addition on the board, with a missing number, e.g. 17 + ☐ = 21.
Read it together. Any child with the missing number card can stand up.
In unison, count on from the smaller to the larger number, holding up one finger for each number. *How many fingers? Four.* Write the missing number. Are the children who are standing up correct?
Repeat for different additions. Is there anyone who has not had an opportunity to stand up?

Multiple nearby!

Missing numbers

Number cards (0 to 9), one set for each pair, number grid (1 to 100)

Children work with their partners.
Write an addition on the board, of a 1-digit number and a multiple of 10. Write the answer, but leave the 1-digit number missing, e.g. 40 + ☐ = 43.
Each pair discusses the addition, and chooses the number card they think matches the missing number.
Say *Show me*, and all the pairs hold up their cards. Write the missing number in the addition.
Repeat for different additions of this kind. Rehearse counting on using a number grid, if necessary.

Whose card?

Ten more or ten less

Number cards (1 to 100), number grid (1 to 100)

Deal one card to each child. Point to a number on the grid and write it on the board. Choose a child to say ten more. Does anyone have the matching card? If so they swap it for a new one. Choose a child to say ten less. Any child with the matching card swap it for a new one. Repeat for different numbers from the grid.

Multiple choice!

Subtracting multiples of ten

A dice, number grid (1 to 100)

Point to a number (more than 60) on the grid and write it on the board, e.g. 64. Choose a child to throw the dice, e.g. 4. We will count back that many tens, i.e. 40. Write three possible answers on the board, e.g. 46, 24, 34. Choose different children to say which they think is correct.

Using the grid count back, in unison, four tens from 64. Who was correct?

Repeat for different numbers (all more than 60).

5 Money

Missing coin!

Coin recognition

Coins (1p to £2, one of each)

Place the coins on a tray, and rehearse the recognition and value of each one.

Ask all the children to shut their eyes, and remove a coin.

When they open their eyes can they guess which coin is missing? Reveal the coin. Who was correct? How did they guess?

Replace the coin and repeat.

Variation: Replace the missing coin with a different coin.

Coins together

Coin recognition

A selection of coins

Choose two children and give them each a
coin, hidden from the rest of the class.
The two children take turns to describe
their coin, e.g. *it is round, it is silver.*
The class guess what the two coins
are, and hence the total. Write some
totals on the board.
The two children reveal their coins.
What were they? What is the total?
Did anyone guess correctly?
Repeat with different children.

Take the same!

Exchange

A selection of coins

Place the coins on a tray. Choose a child and give them a coin (more than
1p), writing the amount on the board. They swap their coin for different
coins from the tray that are equivalent in value. Write these on the board.
Consult the class.
Are they correct?
Are there any
other ways?
Other children
can select
different sets of
coins that are
equivalent in
value. Write
them on the
board.
Repeat with
different
children.

In my pocket

Totals

Tell the children stories about coins you
have in your pocket (use real coins, if
possible).

*In my pocket I have two coins. One is brown,
one is silver. How much could I have?*
The children work in pairs to suggest
different totals. Discuss the possibilities.
Repeat for three coins, or four coins.

Buying cakes

Change

Coins (5p, 10p, 20p)

The children work in pairs. Give each pair a coin: 5p, 10p or 20p.
The cake costs 7p. Write '7p' on the board. *Who cannot afford to buy the
cake?* The pairs with 5p should stand up.
Choose some of the children still sitting. *How much change would you get if
you bought it?* Check
with the class.
Repeat for different
items and prices.

❻ Multiplication and division

Team effort

×2 multiplication facts

Write the multiples of 2 on the board, in two sets: 2, 6, 10, 14, 18 and 4, 8, 12, 16, 20. Divide the class into two teams, one for each set of numbers.

Choose one child from each team to stand at the front, with one hand behind their back. Say *Ready, steady, go*. Each child holds up their hand with a number of fingers standing up, e.g. two and five. Consult the class *What are seven twos? Fourteen*. The team with 14 score a point.

Choose two new children and play again.

Two of the fives!

×5 multiplication facts

Number cards (1 to 10)

Divide the class into five teams. Shuffle the cards and deal two to each team. In turn, choose a child from each team to multiply their first number card by 5. Record the teams' answers on the board. Repeat for the second number cards.

What is each team's total? The team with a total closest to 30 score a point.

Re-deal the cards and play again.

Missing tens

×10 multiplication facts

Write ten ×10 facts on the board, each with a missing number, e.g.
$4 \times 10 = \Box$, $\Box \times 10 = 70$.
Point to a missing number and choose several children to say what they
think it is.
Repeat for each missing number.

Dice chances

Multiplication facts up to 6 × 6

Two dice

Write two lists on the board: 1, 2, 3, ... 10 and 11, 12, 13, ... 36.
Divide the children into two teams, one for each set of numbers. Choose
a child to throw both dice, e.g. 2 and 6. Write the numbers on the board
as a multiplication (i.e. 2 × 6 =) and choose a
child to say the answer, i.e. 12. Check with the
class. The team with the matching number
scores a point.
Continue playing until one team has ten points.

Chains

Halving

There are two rules: if you are passed an even number you halve it and say the answer. If you are passed an odd number, you add one and say the answer.

Choose a child and give them a starter number, e.g. 20. They halve it and pass the answer (10) to the next child. The next child halves it (5) and passes the answer to the next child. That child adds one (6) and passes the number to the next child.

Continue until the chain reaches 1.

Repeat for different starter numbers, e.g. 16, 12, 24. Which numbers give the longest chains?

Towering division

Dividing by grouping

Interlocking cubes, number cards (2, 4, 6, 8, 10, ... 40), number cards (1 to 20)

Children work with their partners.

Deal one card from the even number set to each pair. They take that many cubes and build towers of two. How many towers can they build?

Choose a card at random from the set (1 to 20) and hold it up, e.g. 15. Does anyone have that many towers? Write the division on the board:

$30 \div 2 = 15$.

Repeat for each card.

⑦ Solving problems in real life and measures

I spy
Estimating lengths

Look around the classroom. Say to the children: *I am looking at something that is about 30 cm tall and about 60 cm wide at its widest. Who can tell me what it is?* Children make sensible guesses about what they think it might be. When one child guesses the object (e.g. the hamster cage) they have a turn saying *I spy*.

Animal heights
Adding and subtracting lengths

Choose a child to pretend to be a cat! Give them a large label with a height written on it, e.g. 30 cm. Choose another child to be a dog. Give them a label with a height (e.g. 55 cm), hidden from the rest of the class. Choose another child to be a monkey. Give them a label with a height (e.g. 1 m), hidden from the rest of the class. Tell the class *The dog is 25 cm taller than the cat, and the monkey is 45 cm taller than the dog.* Allow them a few minutes to calculate the heights of the different animals. Repeat with different animals and heights.

Think of a length
Estimating lengths

Number cards (1 to 10), cubes

The children work in groups of three. Choose a group to pick a card, e.g. 6. They read out the number and choose a length, e.g. six metres. Ask other groups to think of something that long, e.g. a van. Award a cube to each group who give a sensible suggestion.

Repeat until all the cards are gone.

Variation: repeat for weight, e.g. six kilograms.

Story time

Solving problems involving measures

Number cards (0 to 9), one set per pair

Tell the children a story:

Once upon a time there was a mother cat. She crept off to her secret nest in the darkest cupboard in the house where she had six kittens. Each kitten weighed half a kilogram. How much do the kittens weigh in total?

Allow the children a few minutes to calculate the answer, and then ask them to hold up a card to match the answer.

Repeat for similar stories (or choose pairs to make up their own), including some involving length.

More time

Solving problems involving time

Number cards (0 to 9), one set per pair

Draw a large alarm clock on the board. Tell the children *You have set your alarm for seven thirty (or half past seven). The dog wakes you up at six o'clock and you are not happy! In order to get back to sleep, you work out how many minutes more sleep you can have. What is the answer?* Allow the children a few minutes thinking time, then ask them to hold up cards to show the answer (i.e. 90).

Play again, with different times.

Magical Mystery Tour

Solving problems involving time

Number cards (3 to 15)

Deal one card to each pair. Explain that everyone is on the 'Magical Mystery Tour' bus. The bus stops every five minutes to let people off! Each pair must look at their card, which is the number of stops they are travelling. Each pair must calculate how long they will be on the bus, by counting in fives. So, if for card '7' they count seven fives – 35 minutes. Choose different pairs to show their cards and say the time, and let them make up a destination, e.g. Manchester United Football ground, Blackpool tower, Alton Towers.

Variation: The bus stops every two minutes, or ten minutes, or three minutes.

Hop timer

Solving problems involving time

Stop watch, or second timer

Choose a child to hop, slowly, ten times – the class can keep count. Time how long it takes, and write the number on the board. Allow each pair a few minutes to calculate how long each hop took. Choose different pairs to answer, and ask them to explain their reasoning.

Next day

Solving problems involving time

A calendar

Each pair chooses a day of the week and writes it down. Turn to a month on the calendar, e.g. June, and say the first day in that month, e.g. *Monday*. Each pair calculates the date on which their day first appears in June (e.g. Wednesday the 3rd, Saturday the 6th).

Repeat, with pairs finding the dates of all their days in a particular month (e.g. 8th, 15th, 22nd, 29th).

Next month

Knowing the months and their order

Sets of month cards (January to December), two dice

Deal one card to each child. Throw one or two dice and call out the number. Any child with the matching month stands up, as quickly as they can (encourage children to work out the number of their month in advance).

Continue until everyone is standing. Rehearse the months in order.

Variation: Children stand up if they have the month before or the month after the number you throw.

Skills Chart

The following chart outlines all the mental skills addressed by the Mental Warm-up activities. The skills are divided into three key areas: place-value and number, addition and subtraction, multiplication and division. The generic activity 'Cross-puzzle' is specifically written to cover a range of skills, and so is not included in this chart.

The chart will assist any teacher looking for an activity dealing with a specific skill. It also makes clear the build-up and sequence of concepts covered throughout the book.

Place-value and Number

Topic	Specific skills	Units
Counting	Counting in ones	N1
	Counting back in ones	N5
	Counting in ones from a 3-digit number	N34
	Counting in twos	N4, N7, N12, N14, N39
	Counting in fives	N15, N26
	Counting in tens	N6, N15, N26, N36, N38
	Counting back in tens	N19
	Counting back in fives	N27
	Counting in fours	N41
	Counting in twenties	N21
	Counting in hundreds	N34
Place-value, ordering, estimating	Recognising the larger and smaller of two numbers	N9
	Rounding to the nearest ten	N36
	Estimating and counting to 10	N28
	Tens and units	N2, N16, N22
Addition	Addition pairs to 10	N3, N10, N18, N31
	Addition pairs to 6	N4
	Adding multiples of 10	N6
	Two more	N7
	Adding 10	N9, N24, N28
	Adding two numbrs up to 20	N10
	Addition pairs to 8	N16

	Addition pairs to 9	N17
	Adding 3	N20
	Addition pairs to 20	N23, N30
	Adding two numbers (crossing 10)	N29
	Adding three 1-digit numbers	N30
	Adding two numbers (up to 20)	N41
	Addition pairs to 10	N37
	Adding 9 or 11	N9, N24, N40
Subtraction	Two less	N2
	Taking away from a number up to 10	N5
	Taking away 10	N11, N28
	Difference	N33
	Taking away 1	N19
	Taking away from a number up to 20	N27
	Taking away to make a multiple of 10	N33
	Taking away 9 or 11	N11, N28
Money	Using fewest coins to make a total	N11
	Totals and change	N14, N18, N23, N29
	Coin recognition	N3, N21, N32
Multiplication	Multiplying by 2	N13
	Multiplying by 5	N25
	Multiplying by 10	N39
	Doubling	N8, N12, N17, N32, N35
	Halving	N40